The Supe

The Superhero Lover

Explicit Behavior
In Between the Sheets

Shaun Saunders

Shaun Saunders
Atlanta, GA

The Superhero Lover

Cover design by TLH Designs, Chicago, IL (www.tlhdesigns. com)

Book design by Kingdom Living Publishing, Accokeek, MD (www.kingdomlivingbooks.com)

For information about this book or to contact the author, send an email to thesuperherolover@gmail.com.

Published by:

Shaun Saunders
Atlanta, GA

Published in the United States of America.

ISBN 978-0-692-77960-6

Contents

Foreword

The Superhero Lover is a powerful story about love and the sanctity of marriage from a biblical standpoint. Rev. Shaun Saunders uses his faith, beliefs, and the power of God's word while telling a unique story of the ups and downs of being married. He allows his readers to understand that God's love for man meant for him not to be alone, but to find a help mate, partner, best friend, and lover to navigate life's temptations and pitfalls.

Rev. Saunders uses his understanding of marriage from a personal outlook. He shows that regardless of your status in life, every married couple has doubts about being with only one person for the rest of their life. This is a compelling story about love and marriage from a pastor's perspective. He shows that even Superheroes are not immune to the challenges and fears that come with being married.

Teresa Ferrell-Wright

Introduction

To all my single Ladies, adorned with a sultry pizazz, the sexy, that has manipulated the Superhero to pursue after a fantasy stimulated by your seduction: It is official! The Superhero Lover has closed the door once opened to a plethora of many beautiful delicacies made easily available to him in a variety of deliciously scrumptious flavors. After flirting around with one scoop of French Vanilla, two scoops of that Butter Pecan, and three scoops of that Strawberry Deluxe, the Superhero Lover's taste buds that used to uncontrollably grope and salivate over a new flavor each week have now come to rediscover that loving feeling with that one flavor with whom he has longed to become reacquainted. Finally, after tasting and testing for the quality, falsely advertised within each of a multiplicity of options from which he picked and decided to choose from, the Superhero Lover looked all over and found that Sexually Chocolate flavor specifically manufactured to quench his thirst and satisfy his pleasure. She, standing at an estimated height of 5'5", captivated by the glow of her caramel complexion and the sweat oozing through the pores of her gorgeous flesh, dripping like melted ice cream down the seam of her curvaceous thighs, the Superhero declares with a swagger in his countenance that she makes him weak in the knees. The beauty of an eternal flame ignited by the fire they make when united is the sweet smell of love burning and fusing together the Superhero Lover and his unknown love interest, whom for now we can only identify her as the Sexy and Vivacious Ms. Destiny. With his wounds revealed through the eyes of his alter ego and the admitted confession in what was an extremely intense tell-all exclusive interview with his arch nemesis, the Superhero has found love, and for reasons unknown, is ready to reveal to the world the details of his explicit behavior in between the sheets with the Sexy and Vivacious Ms. Destiny.

So to all my single ladies and yes to the one, two, maybe three, four, okay five or more unhappily married ladies attempting to dethrone their present suitor, passionately declaring and selfishly convinced that God said the Superhero really is the one for me: KA BOOM! The Superhero Lover's sweet lady has stepped up in the room affirmed by God that she is what you thought you were, but never had and never ever will have a chance to become. Ladies and Gentleman, it is with great joy that I present to you the Superhero Lover and his uncensored conversation with us about his Explicit Behavior in Between the Sheets!

As media networks slowly begin to gather intel on the identity of the Superhero's destined lover, a swarm of paparazzi flock to multiple locations where it has been reported the two have been known to spend time together, places where some would presume they get their freak on. Each reporter is anxious to be the first to capture that million-dollar photo of the two that will reveal the secret identity of the Superhero's special, special lady. "Just who is this special lady," a question former flames and past desires begin asking each other. Then all of a sudden out of nowhere the ignorance of that one, the one chick he dated, but wished he never met, who continues to stalk his every move day and night, lethargically sings out, "She must have put it on him and gave him that good love...." Her comment countered with the response of "shut your mouth," as someone in the crowd yells out in an effort to dismiss her inappropriate comments by expelling her unlawful intentions towards manipulating the integrity of his story's context.

So, just who is this phenomenal woman to whom the Superhero has happily divided the responsibility of his crown, overjoyed at the privilege he has been granted to walk alongside his queen as her King? This skillfully crafted masterpiece intricately woven together, clothed in the extremely well-compacted shape of a species called woman, is the epitome of the Superhero's modern day Cinderella, a woman graced to walk in a glass shoe fit only for the prince's princess.

Now with an unusually healthy infatuation with the woman to whom he boastfully presumes to be the one, the Superhero gradually maneuvers from the mystique of a lone ranger into the titillating posture of a sex symbol exemplifying the beauty found within the absent art of fidelity. Like young love, deceived by the ecstasy and the unending possibility of loves promises, the Superhero's rebellious motion against society's replacement of monogamy in exchange for the uncontrollable urges of promiscuity inspires women worldwide to revolt against the idea that all men are dogs, once exposed to the reality of the hero's chivalrous stand. After years of women submitting to men unworthy of their submission, the interest in the Superhero's new love has attracted women of all ages to the kind of dog every woman should aspire for their man to be. I know most of the women are probably saying, "Oh no he did not! What did he just say?" Before you, however, decide to close this book, allow me to explain.

The saying "all men are dogs" is a true statement. There is, however, a difference between a stray dog and a trained dog. A stray dog wanders about without a destination or a purpose, unruly, undisciplined, unlawfully released from the grip of his master leash. This dog in a man lustfully pursues after any available tail, intent on chasing after the kitty cat, selfishly craving the sensation of that explosion achieved at the peak of his sexual climax. He is comforted more by the assurance of being pleased without ever satisfying his Lady Love's pleasure.

A trained dog, on the other hand, is disciplined pursuing only after the purpose sanctioned for him at the command of his master voice. His desire lies only in whatever his master desires for him to have. When the master calls, he comes, because his desire is to please his master. This dog in a man is intent on epitomizing the richness of fidelity, loyalty, and the grace encompassed around a beauty that enables two separate identities to become one. Now all those bag ladies who once concluded that all men are dogs cultivated from the same breed have begun to divorce themselves from the unpredictability of the stray they were so naively convinced they could change from the stereotypical posture of a pitiful frog into the irresistible fantasy of their prince charming. They have been inspired by the Superhero's dedication to love and encouraged, once again, to believe in love's possibility for themselves.

"THERE THEY ARE! THERE THEY ARE! One of the *Daily Times* Most Diabolical Reporters yells out, causing a host of news reporters and followers to move expeditiously toward the location where they are convinced the two love birds are currently hiding. As they excitedly converge onto the once undisclosed location, hoping to see and hear from the dynamic duo about the love they share, they find the area clear, void of any evidence to show that the Superhero and his destined lover were ever there in the first place.

"All Hell No, We Just Got Played!" Reporters furiously scream out succumbing to the reality that they had just been hoodwinked by that, that scum of a reporter. The Accuser, a top notch reporter for the *Daily Times* and the Superhero's number one arch nemesis, has once again employed the art of deception in an attempt to buy some time to work up a plan to distort the reemergence of this idea called real love. As he secretly searches out their whereabouts, to his surprise the sound of a rushing, mighty wind of frustrated reporters accompanied by former flames loosed from their makeup, earrings, and Red Bottom Pumps—all those to whom he had maliciously sent off on a meaningless excursion—come back, frantically charging down on him. As they approach with what seems to be tongues of fire resting on them, declaring together in unison, "WE ARE GOING TO KICK YOUR... (beep, beep) ......" they violently close in on his location. Surrounded by an angry mob of reporters and the burned out flames of past desires, the Accuser shakes violently in fear, afraid the angry crowd is going to take his life.

Just when the crowd was ready to beat this fool down, they are unsuspectingly interrupted by the innocent cries of a child melodically singing and pointing out, "THERE!" drawing the attention of the group from the Accuser onto the designated place where the Superhero Lover and the lovely Mrs. Destiny have decided to reveal themselves. With the echo of the young lad's words ringing in their ears, they all at once, move with remarkable precision. Turning their heads in unison, they fix their eyes towards the radiant glow that unexpectedly overshadows them, shining from the direction where the innocent child had previously pointed. Like the contagious zeal of diehard fans anxiously awaiting the moment when their most beloved entertainer makes his way onto the stage, the determined crowd violently rushes, with no regard for human life, towards the red carpet as they rejoice excited about the opportunity to witness, live and in person, the processional of the phenomenal hero and his leading Lady.

As the light of day begins to dim into the darkness of night, its silence is interrupted by the two superstars' show-stopping entrance onto a stage capable of holding up under the glory of their moment. As they make their way down the legendary red carpet, spectators, blessed to behold the beauty of their union, stand in awe, almost in disbelief, captivated by the radiant array of dazzling colors shining from the rock resting on her third finger left hand. With reporters racing to be the first to capture this breaking news and all the ladies stilled by the size of her ring, concluding he must have really liked it, so he went and put a ring on it, the Superhero gently places his hand on her waist and pulls her body close to his, confirming his role as her source, sustainer, and protector, while redirecting the media's attention back to the colorful glow accompanying their love.

Leaning towards him, trusting that when she falls into his arms, she will be guaranteed the highest level of security and safety, she draws closer to her disguised Hercules with an angelic stare. She looking at him like a deliciously scrumptious meal she would like to eat as he becomes an impersonation in her mind of her DeAngelo, waiting for her to tell him, "How Does It Really Feel?" graciously maneuvers her well-figured frame into the clutches of his masculine embrace. Without every speaking a word, she serenades her boo with a seductive baby you give good love to me bedroom stare that makes all the ladies go "Awwwww" and all the fellows go "That's my dude!" The two, now standing united as one, spiritually, emotionally, and sexually stimulated by the extreme sensitivity they encounter when standing in one another's presence, engage in a wet kiss, giving fans, reporters, and former flames the confirmation they needed to affirm that she was the most reasonable option he saw fit to choose for himself.

The crowd now resting in their eternal bliss,

caught up in the moment of their kiss, echoing the sound of love heard around the world is suddenly disrupted by the inappropriate gestures of an unmoved reporter yelling out to his cameraman, "Wake up and take the picture you, idiot." The cameraman discombobulated, with slobber running down the side of his chin, imagining what it would be like to rest a juicy wet one all up on the silhouette of the sexy and vivacious Ms. Destiny's luscious lips awakes out of his stupor, focuses his camera lens and takes the shot, making one bright flash. In an effort to hush the crowd, the Superhero cordially lifts his hands and slowly lowers them respectfully demanding everyone's attention as he reveals the magnitude of his love for his Destiny lover in this melodious poetic discourse entitled *The One!*

"Sexy as all H-E-L-L, smooth like a fresh bottle of baby oil gently applied on a baby's backside, a brick house poise with an amazing lady-like posture that would make even a dead man cry out in the words of Maya Angelou, *"And Still I Rise."*" The epitome of an internal beauty that oozes like dew gently resting upon the skin of her exterior posture has inspired me to dance in motion with the rhythm of her heartbeat. Tick, Tick, Tock! The time on my clock has expired; the pain of past relationships I no longer desire. Now no longer alone warmed by the flame ignited by her fire I salute this, my sweet lady, this my extremely sophisticated, strikingly intelligent, sexually captivating, and Holy Ghost intoxicated queen. She is my Queeeeeeeen to be. She is my Mrs. Destiny. She is the only suitable help I always needed to rescue me from the P-I-M-P I thought I was or perhaps thought I could be. So today, let's make it official! Ladies and Gentlemen get up on your feet for my Boo, my baby girl. Here she is, to all the Ladies, it is over, it is done. Today I introduce and reveal to the world the arrival of my destiny of whom I announce to you all as "The One."

Let's go! It is time to turn up, in this my third installation in the life of the Superhero Lover and his Destined Lover.

All This Love Is Waiting for You!

Session One

"He who finds a [true] wife finds a good thing and obtains favor from the Lord" (Proverbs 18:22).

With the reverberating sound of Love's Kiss re-emerging after society's exile and the denunciation of it as a relevant idea, the Superhero's proclamation of love is challenged by the recipient of its reception, when she seeks to discover the sincerity of his answer after asking him the question, "Do you really love me, and if so how much?" Under the assumption that most men would ignorantly respond by saying, "Yes I do," while projecting some unmeasurable numerical value like, "I love you unconditionally" to convince the recipient of their treasure that their love has no limits, the Superhero perceives that her motivation for asking was only to confirm the answer to the real question she wanted to ask, but fearing her interrogation might cause love to change his mind, she decided not to ask: To what extent are you willing to love me to and at what point in our relationship will your love decide to walk away, stop, or cease to exist?

Like most women, Mrs. Destiny poses to her love, what for most men would be somewhat of a threatening question, searching to discover what his love demands from her, and the conditions under which his love requires her to abide by in order for love not to change its mind. As he cautiously moves to answer, clearly aware of what she expects and would consider as an acceptable response, he, smooth like Billy Dee in *Mahogany*, utters, in the words of Bell, Biv, and Devo, these words to secure her faith in this love to which he himself is uncertain if whether or not he has confidently secured: "I really do love you; I really do need you, with words I can't explain. So let me show you throughout our life together how much, I do love you." After gracing her with his Rico Suave swag, serenading her with an exceptional eloquence and his harmonious wordplay, she falls under his spell, hypnotized by the ecstasy of love's promising possibility. Though extremely captivated by his MAC DADDY words, she wonders if his current posture, with time, will either prove to be true or the disguise he used to add her to an already long list of clients emotionally seduced by the arrogance of his PIMP DADDY character.

Assured by God that their union was His desire Mrs. Destiny still proceeds slowly and carefully with the dispensing of her love towards her Lover, not allowing her emotions to prematurely cause her to become so easily submissive once again to an illusion of love to which she has become all too familiar. As they walk into the genesis of their journey down the Yellow Brick Road of love, seeming always as they begin to disappear into the distance of destiny, accompanied by their theme song, *Happy Feelings*, echoed through the heavenly voices of Frankie Beverly and Maze, Mrs. Destiny, like Lot's wife, though moving forward, has a tendency of looking back, as a result of previous experiences on this roller coaster ride called love. Waiting to hear that salutation of love from her Superhero Lover that will cause her joy to leap in the same way as Elizabeth, whose baby John leaped while in her womb after hearing the salutation of Mary, the mother of Jesus, she gracefully glides with a resounding countenance beside her He-Man, watching carefully to discover the truth of his answer to the question: How Do You Love Me?

With Ms. Destiny heavily exploring the possibility of becoming Mrs. Lover, an idea recommended by her suitor who has in the words of El Debarge declared to her that, All his Love Is and Has Been

Waiting for her, they journey down the elaborate hall of holy matrimony with an excitement, driven by the emotional ecstasy that escorts love in its premier into the holiness of marital bliss. "The Bride is coming; the bride is coming!" The innocent proclamation of a youthful lad initiating the bridal processional accompanied by the echoing sound of Dun dun dun dun dun dun dun dun fueling the expectancy of their guest awaiting the appearing of the queen.

Standing, eagerly anticipating her unveiling, the usually inevitable ovation for the bride from the decadent marital entourage is disrupted by a host of uninvited Ladies who sarcastically began to reminisce on their past encounters with the Superhero Lover, to whom they all used to refer more formidably to as "Big Papa." Before she enters the room, where she presumes all those gathered are there to support their nuptial ceremonial service, she is notified of the potential threat of all notable imposters identified on the surveillance footage taken from a secret location, as she proceeds cautiously prioritizing the severity of each threat within the coded dimension of its COLORED CATEGORY! Just what is the COLORED CATEGORY? I am glad you asked. First, the coded dimension found within the colored categories mentioned above, more commonly referred to as the female intuition or the sixth sense, is Ms. Destiny's gut feeling regarding the dysfunctional dietary infatuations of her hero, who used to be an overweight lover, a glutton, motivated by an uncontrollable appetite to feast on what at first glance looked sweet but left a sour taste in his mouth. It is at this point that Ms. Destiny is exposed to a limited sample of each of the many flavors he had ignorantly decided to choose from.

Finally, as her escapade from the bridal bunker comes to a standstill at the altar of the unknown, she accommodated by the muscle of her stubborn father, who would much rather see her alone and in love with Jesus, than to marry anyone let alone a Superhero, stands eager and anxious for what every woman aspiring to be married would call the Great Exchange. Defined, the Great Exchange is the public relinquishing of a father's rights to provide legally for the services of the bride, his daughter, over to the man, to whom he presumes to be worthy enough to man up under the weight of her submission.

As they all converge onto the scene at the throne of the altar, Ms. Destiny, with her hand tightly entwined with that of her father, he paralyzed by the fear of letting his little girl go, now standing face-to-face with the Superhero who waits anxiously for the ceremonial changing of the guard to begin, they turn an about face towards the officiating minister when asked that one question that initiates the process of the Great Exchange. "Who is it that gives this woman to be wedded to this man?" This is a question, today, that is seldom asked, but answered with the silencing sound of a father's absence. Standing, blessed to behold this his baby girl's special day, humbled by the sacredness of their matrimonial union, he having earned the privilege to flex his patriarchal muscle, says, "I do, do, do, do" echoing for all the privileged witnesses once again the masculine unappreciated gift of Father's authoritative voice just as he releases her from the overly protective grip of his safety for the last time.

As he does so, he exhales what appears to be the promise of his wrath oozing like ferociously hot steam thrusting from his nostrils, fueled by the uncertainty of her suitor's protection. His promise serving as a sign of warning to her King to strongly consider the consequences of any unlawful action he better not even think to make against his daughter that would cause daddy to afflict upon him some bodily harm. With a long, intimidating stare, he shouts out loudly for all to hear, "If you every hurt my baby girl, I am going to kick your ....!" This statement accompanied by his vengeful posture and his gesturing threats giving the Groom fair notice that for every move he makes, every breath he takes, and every bond he breaks daddy sure nuff will be watching him.

With a gasping for air sound, the exhaling spectators are finally released from the intoxicating nausea of holding their breath, paralyzed by the brides' father's eloquently intimidating doctoral dissertation that was spoken for an audience of one, but witnessed by all. The guests, now, all at once turn toward the man of the hour, anxious to see if whether or not he can come back with a response that would vindicate him from the realities of this cruel but lawful indictment. With all eyes on the Superhero lover, he quickly re-establishes his position, reaffirming for all his skeptics the security of his defensive stance after being hit with a flurry of body shots that caused his knees to buckle and his legs to wobble, wobble.

After thoughtfully considering what might be his most appropriate reaction under the circumstances, the Superhero lover maintains his integrity up under his father-in-law's allegedly premature allegations, confirmed by his demeanor forever pleading his innocence promising never ever to provide anyone with any form of circumstantial evidence that would prove him guilty of all the charges of which he could possibly be accused. Conscious of the good and the bad of those awarded the privilege of currently participating in or the failed attempts of those having participated in marriage once before, he decides to qualify his candidacy as Ms. Destiny's first man with minimal words determined to prove throughout time the depth of his love by dismissing those exaggerations of marriages instability enforced upon him by those who have painfully experienced its chance.

Now with the atmosphere purified and their love demanding the attention of those in love, those wanting to be loved, and those crippled by the idea of love's possibility, blessed to behold love again in its purest form, they finally meet right on time at the altar to which they both were destined at this time to be. Standing unashamed, they draw closer to each other and share an intimate stare that causes everyone to acknowledge the insignificance of their presence in a room of what appeared to be reserved for only two. As the Superhero Lover and Ms. Destiny stand elevated on a rotating stage, consumed with a full fill of the illusion of love's wonder, both men and women mesmerized by the conviction of their iconic stare, serenaded by the sound of Stevie Wonder's *"You and I"* echoing for all to hear the voice of God affirming that this is the kind of love with which He is well pleased, the crowd begins weeping uncontrollably, shedding tears in the name of love. Yes, love, the word so many people have used in vain has pressed softly upon the hardened heart of the once misogynistic masculinity of all the men residing in the room, deflating the ego of their male chauvinist personality into the innocence of their neglected inner child crying out of his need to be loved. With the failed attempts of these men to continuously uphold their macho, macho man posterior, afraid their show of tears might be used as a weapon to castrate their masculinity, they quickly move to disguise their overwhelming show of emotions by responding to that tricky question that every man dreads, "Are you crying?" All the men respond with an answer of "Man please, I just have something in my eye."

In a blatant effort to maneuver away from a venue, now flooded by the showers of secure, but a reluctantly emotional, group of men, the reverend presiding over the service moves to continue with the ceremony, asking if there is anyone present who sees any reason why the two should not wed to please speak now or forever hold their peace. As he pauses briefly, to grant the attendees time to respond to his very poignant question, a young man jumps up, wiping the tears from his face, as he yells out, "I OBJECT," causing an echo of "What" to resonate in the demeanor of the crowd standing in disbelief. The Reverend proceeds to calm everyone's nerves by asking the distraught male on what grounds he believes the uniting of these two would be unjustified. The offender then moves to the middle of the aisle, accompanied by what at first appears to be two security guards and then, to everyone's surprise, he begins to dance, putting on his best rendition of Chris Brown's BET Awards performance, justifying his objection by declaring "*These Girls Ain't Loyal.*" "Man if you don't sit your goofy hind parts down and stop that nonsense," the Superhero Lover yells out, silencing the ignorance of this imposter's unreasonable logic, and informing the reverend to continue with the service. This young lad, who later is identified as the Accuser, the Daily Times most diabolical reporter, was immediately removed from the premises singing on his way out the door, "*I got nothing but love for you baby.*"

After the dust settled and the smoke cleared, the Reverend proceeds by asking again, to everyone surprises, "Now, if there is anyone else who would like to object to this union, please do so without all the shenanigans." Just then one of the guests in the front row sarcastically yells out, "Are you crazy?" he confused about why, after all, that just happened, the reverend would be dumb enough to ask that question again. Fortunately, after asking that question a second time, no one in the audience made any objections to the union in which these two were about to embark on.

After reciting their vows and exchanging rings, the Reverend announces to the Superhero Lover, those words every groom looks forward to hearing, "You may kiss your bride." Lifting up her veil, the Superhero Lover leans in and lays a juicy wet one on his bodacious bride, preparing her for the good loving she was going to get later that night. As they turn and face all their witnesses, the Reverend introduces the newlyweds to an audience ready to explode in jovial celebration: "Ladies and gentlemen I introduce to you, for the first time Mr. and Mrs. Loverrrrrrrrrrrrrrrrrrrr!" Like an explosion, the crowd breaks out into a riotous celebratory shout, mingled with the applauded tears of joyful admiration and the awkward sadistic narcissism of those waiting for it not to work just so they can say, "I told you so." After all they went through to make it to this point surely the moment they had been waiting for had finally come.

As the reception night fever settles down and their wedding guests begin heading home, the bride and the groom find themselves in the company of one another at the center of the dance floor, serenaded by the last song of the night, Bill Withers' *"Just the Two of Us."* Confident they can make if they just try, the Superhero escorts his bride to their master quarters, where it is about TO GO DOWN! Ready to take a dive into what he believes is a private pool for which he would be the first and last ever to swim in, he entices her with a little bump and grind to sync her body with the rhythm of his stroke. With eyes of legal lust, burning with that Rick James and Tina Marie kind of *"Fire and Desire,"* they enter their love chamber, leaving a do not disturb sign on the door warning all possible threats of interruption that it is our honeymoon so do not bother because we are about to blow each other's mind!"

You Blow My Mind

Session Two

*"Let marriage be held in honor (esteemed worthy,
precious, of great price, and especially dear) in all
things. And thus let the marriage bed be undefiled
(kept undishonored); for God will judge and punish the
unchaste [all guilty of sexual vice] and adulterous*
(Hebrews 13:4 AMP).

Boom, boom, boom! The echoing sound of that good
loving standing at the door of their master suite bent
on satisfying their curiosity by releasing sexual stimuli that cause each of their bodies to pulsate uncontrollably. Ready to dance to the rhythm of multiple
emotional and physical orgasms, accompanied by the
soulful vocals of Maxwell's, *"MelloSmooth"* they seek
to set the tone in an atmosphere created exclusively
for lovers only. Entering into the corridors of their
love chambers, in awe, stunned by the excellence of
this long awaited moment, though they would like to

quickly consummate their marriage, they approach this their first time together sexually, carefully, intent on satisfying the pleasures of one another. "Wow, this is amazing," Mrs. Destiny excitedly declares as she informs her lover, on her way to the bedroom that she is going to change into something she assures him, he is going to like. With his fire and desire already sizzling hot, intensified by the added fuel of her provocative comment, the Superhero moves quickly to prepare himself to ROCK HER WORLD and BLOW HER MIND.

After a few sit-ups, pushups, and an excessive application of baby oil smothered all over his muscular frame, the Superhero proceeds aggressively towards Mrs. Destiny, following the lead of his Alpha maleness, to initiate contact. As he steps into the room, accompanied by R. Kelly's *"Seems Like You Ready"* playing in the background, ready to take a dive into the deep seas of his lovers unexplored beauty, set on releasing his sexual beast on her freak lying beyond the depths of her curvaceous extremities" he smoothly glides into the room singing. Greased up like he bathed in a tub of Crisco oil, he awkwardly slides, stumbling to maintain his balance, into the master chambers, where to his surprise he can see Mrs. Destiny has anxiously, a-n-x-i-o-u-s-l-y been awaiting his arrival. With his eyes wide open, fixed on her body and her booty, and his mind like, "Whaaaaaaat," he drooling wipes his mouth and understands that he did not need to ask her if she was ready because SHE WAS READY! The Superhero, caught off guard by her initiative and preparedness, had to reexamine himself again to see if he was really ready to handle all this good loving she was about to put on him.

As he questions his readiness, she moves with a bounce, pop, and a seductive switching of her thighs, one rubbing against the other, towards him ready to give him the best loving he has never had. Her lingerie covered just enough of the hunted parts of her body, she intent on intriguing her officer and her gentleman to perform a legal search and frisk of her premises in order for the two of them to inflict their fantasies up on the enticed flesh of the other as they seek to commit indecent acts of lawful exposure that they both anticipate will lead to unimaginable sexual pleasure. As the heat of their passion that night burned out of control like a raging fire, they begin this, their wild bull ride, with an innocent kiss teaching each other all about the melodious sounds of love!

I LOVE IT WHEN YOU CALL ME BIG PAPA, Big Daddy, Ai Papai or Mr. Big Stuff, all of those endearing terms every male lover longs to make his woman scream, inaugurating his masculine big headed ego into the office of her Mandingo warrior. As he rocks the boat and strokes the insides of her satiable anatomy, overwhelmed with the skill of his motion amidst the deep depths of her ocean, she maneuvers into a superior position that will enable her to tame that wild stallion with some of her whip appeal. As she moves like the windy beat of a long-awaited wave, her Mandingo surfer sexually connects with the rhythm of her stroke and they become one just as they begin to, in the words of R&B superstar Usher, reach their climax. With the oneness of their bodies inseparably fused together, Mrs. Destiny with the Janet Jackson *"Funny How Time Flies When You're Having Fun"* end of the song moan and the Superhero looking like a retarded Aaron Hall singing, Ba-be tease me tonight, they arrive at the pinnacle of their sexual mountain simultaneously exploding, both high like an addict addicted to that first hit of that drug that pleased his pleasure. After conquering their sexual mountain, they quickly descend from their climb assuming, because of their marital newness that the ease with which they climbed to their peak will not be challenged by unexpected obstacles every time they tried to climb up again, after the first time.

As an author and Pastor, I do understand that for some the details of the Superhero Lover's sexual escapade with his wife, the lovely, sexy, and vivacious Mrs. Destiny, may cause discomfort or even cause others to ask, "Why would he choose to discuss the details on what some presume to be such an inappropriate topic as sex?" Some of you may even be concluding in your own Holiness that, "Surely God does not have anything to do with this? This is unholy and ungodly." Or better yet, my favorite, "That's the Devil!" So for all of you who disagree, particularly church folks, if you would please answer the following questions: If Sex is not godly, then why did God create it? If sex is a topic that the church should not discuss, then please explain to us how did you get here? Besides, if the truth were to be told, even the sanctified get horny and want to do it, desiring, in the words of Ginuwine, to take a pony ride or have someone ride on their pony.

Sex, when used within the legal parameters of a Godly context, the only channel through which God intended for it to be used, is not only a good thing but a great thing. God created it, stupid, and He created it only for the pleasure of those invested in the perfect context of Holy matrimony. The word "context" means the circumstances under which privileged behavior is awarded to individuals who have legally entered into a flawless institution designed by God. Sex is Good, but when it is used outside of the right context; i.e., marriage, it becomes a bad thing through which the forces of evil thrive. This is why Satan tries to encourage so many of us to indulge in sex prematurely, getting us to participate in a good thing, just at the wrong time (out of context), making it a bad thing.

Due to the silence or the lack of enlightenment that should be provided by the church on this topic and the openly sexual and prematurely exposed generation ambushed with the overwhelming pressure of anything goes sexuality, sex throughout time has become a big time business instead of a luxury for lovers who have chosen to love legally. With human trafficking and porn generating billions globally per year, the rise of the LGBT community, sexual exploitation over the internet, and the acceptance of a host of sexually promiscuous television shows, it is obvious that the church has dropped the ball on a topic that has left the church guessing, looking like a dumb deer in headlights. Let me state this clearly: Sex is a physical union, created by God to be shared only between a man and a woman in marriage for procreation and pleasure. Sex is permissible only in marriage because marriage is honorable among all and its bed is undefiled.

Marriage is Honorable! The word honorable is defined, according to its use in the context of the sentence used previously, as something of good standing, influential, wealthy, and respectable. It is the institution that God created and intended to be more highly esteemed, even above the presumed value of the one with which this union is to be entered. It is the most suitable union through which life is to be conceived, the rock of the healthy family upon which strongly fortified societies stand. A change in one's feelings or opinion regarding a partner's dysfunction is never an acceptable excuse to remove oneself from such an honorable institution because it is supposed to be respected more than the respect the two in love claim to have for one another. Unfortunately, in the world we live in today marriage is not honored as it should be. Couples respect their emotions more than they respect God's credible institution. Feelings change because people change, but the only consistent thing that forever remains the same is marriage when it is esteemed more honorable than the devices that try to cripple its success. In other words, marriage is to be respected, even more than the respect that two individuals have for one another because it is God's projected model for every couple's success.

Marriage is the only appropriate context through which two individuals of the opposite sex can honor God through the artistry of sexual intercourse. When the two individuals joined together honor the institution of marriage, then the bed they occupy together in the marriage is undefiled because legally they have the right to cohabitate in the space of one another's dwelling. In the original Greek, the word *"undefiled"* means "to be free from that which the nature of a thing is deformed and debased, or its force and vigor impaired."

Marriage has been drastically re-defined, unwisely rooted in a phrase coined by one of America's founding fathers, Thomas Jefferson, who declared within the framework of the Declaration of Independence that all men are created equal. Interestingly enough on June 26, 2015, the U.S. Supreme Court ruled that same-sex couples can marry nationwide, establishing a new civil right and handing gay rights advocates a historic win. The verdict defends that because all are created equal, marriage for same-sex couples is just as honorable as the traditional marriage model because of that coined phrase. The question then that one must ask is just what does all men created equal mean in the eyes of God. According to Scripture all men, both men, and women, are created equal in substance, but both have been designated to fulfill two distinctly different roles of responsibility within the mandated mission of the Master. The continued existence of the two is determined by the existence of one another, or else the natural order of humanity would become extinct. So then, both are equal in substance because the value of each gender's contribution to the other is the same. Scripture clearly states *"It is not good for man to be alone"* and so God then provided for the man, who was alone, a Suitable Help! The word "alone" means to exist in isolation, to be kept in the company of oneself, or to live in the absence of a sufficient help necessary for man to successfully adhere to a request that would confirm the purpose of his existence. God, therefore, built for man, pulling a rib from the interior of his body and to reveal within the context of his reality the woman, a man with a womb, a Fe-Male or a male with a fetus. God formed man, and out of His concern for his well-being, built from the same substance, an opposite but compatible anatomy stacked just right with all, yes all, the resources he needed. God pulled out of Adam his womb-man, so Adam could make no excuse for looking inside of himself to rediscover what God intentionally pulled out of him, placed beside him, and then specifically commanded these two to be fruitful and increase in number; fill the earth and subdue it. This is the natural order of marriage.

Every day the sun rises and sets, plants release oxygen, women give birth, birds soar, and fish swim. All these things are natural because every day they guarantee the possibility of continuing to reproduce the same results. The natural order of a man and woman, joining in marriage, guarantees the possibility of love's continuity because of their ability to reproduce naturally in others an expression of the love they share. This enables love to continue to exercise its right to abide from generation to generation based on the foundation of the God defined family. On the other hand, however, the legalization of same-sex marriage is unnatural because these two with the same anatomy cannot naturally reproduce an expression of the love they claim to share. Once their days on this earth come to an end, it is a guaranteed impossibility that a successor will emerge from their union. Listen to play baseball; you need at least a ball and a glove. The ball without the glove or the glove without the ball disqualifies both players from playing the game due to the insufficiency of the equipment. Every man needs a woman's womb, and every woman needs to be touched with the scepter of her knight in shining armor. So to all my brothers and sisters in the LBGT community, I sincerely love you, but I do not support you. Marriage, in God's eyes, will only be legal when entered into by one man and one woman. Christians do not hate you. How can we? The Scripture says, "*Such were some of us*," but with that said, it is important for you to understand that no matter what the Supreme Court's decision is, no man can redefine what God has already clearly defined. Marriage is honorable and the bed undefiled only when the union is shared between a man and a woman.

After debriefing one another at the bottom of their mountain high from which they had just come down, the Superhero like any newly wedded husband curious to get his lovers feedback on how he believes he laid it down, parenthetically declares, "I've been to the mountaintop, and I believe you got there with me, but if not we need to keep on doing our love thing so that we as a couple can get to the mountaintop together!" Deceived, convinced that sex and love are inseparable and denying the possibility that there is any difference between the two of them, the Superhero confidently assumes that he has proven the integrity of his love by making her body whistle to the echoing sound of her speaking in tongues. Careful not to dethrone her self-proclaimed

Mandingo from the seat of his throne, she questioning how long before he changes after tasting those delicious chocolate chips in her cookies, cautiously announces to her He-Man, "Babe you pleased me, but it is going to take a life time of loving for you to satisfy all this boo, boo!"

Shocked and stunned, falling off his high horse, cradled by the humiliation of believing he failed to satisfy her with the sexual healing she desired, he is left speechless, rambling and stuttering as he tries to figure out what to say. "Babe, babe, so what, let me get this right, what I think you are trying to say is, uhm is that, but you were like ooh I love you, big papa, so what you did not mean that? I know you are not saying that I did not Rock Your World, because you know I put it down on yah! So, just what do you mean when you say I pleased you, but you are not satisfied? Seeing how her comment deflated the confident stride of his Macho man from the swagger of his Mandingo, she quickly interrupts her misinformed lover. "Babe no, no, no! No babe, you laid it down, but your sex and your loving are not synonymous. You pleased my body, but how you choose to love me from this point forward, after taking a swim in between the deep seas of my uninhabited waters, will determine if whether or not you have the wherewithal to satisfy me, boo! That is what I was trying to say?" After reinstating the confidence of her man, who at first took her unexplained comment as a blatant attempt to castrate his manhood, she slightly reframing a question she had asked him once before asks, "Did you believe you when you said you love me? I sure hope you meant what you said because I can assure you that loving me is not going to be as easy as walking in the park. It may be easy now for you to sing, *"If loving me is wrong then you do not want to be right,"* but are you certain that you will still love me when my hair turns gray? Will you still want me if I gain a little or a lot of weight? What if I cannot or am not in the mood to allow you to massage the interior walls of my poo nah nee or caress the fur of my kitty cat with your magic wand? Will you love me after the kids, when I do not feel like cleaning, when I am sad, mad as hell, when I'm not feeling you, or you are not feeling me, when I am tired, when I don't feel like cooking, or, yes, when I have to remind you that I'm not your Superwoman? Yea, babe you give good love to me, and honey I am sorry to have to tell you this, but that is not enough! I need that and so, so much more. Plain and simply Boo, you got to show me what you're working with!"

Understanding her concern, but questioning the timing of her need to voice it, the Superhero, feeling like he just got pimp slapped with this challenging discourse, is confronted with the dubious task of putting together the right words that will convince her to believe in this love of which he has not yet convinced her to be certain. Never before having to think this fast on his feet, to find the words to say, the mood in the room becomes awkward, due to his silence as she sits staring, waiting for him to man up and say something that will let her know that he has her covered.

It is important here to insert that love is not a falling feeling, but an action that expresses a consciously calculated effort towards a designated recipient, worthy of its sacrifice. This is why the statement "I fell in love" is an invalid declaration. To fall into something indicates that there is no control by an individual to choose whom he or she will decide to love. No one has control of where or how he or she will land when falling. Falling eliminates love from the human reasoning as the luxury of something I do because I choose to, exchanging its truth with the fallacy of an uncontrolled emotion that chose love for me as a result of an uncontrolled circumstance happening in my life at a designated time. Loving somebody costs and I am sure that those who have chosen to love would agree that the objective to whom they have extended their love is worthy of its sacrifice.

Likewise, the objective to which a man is willing to become vulnerable in order to extend the sacrifice of his love towards, will always render objections to the origin of love's projections until she is convinced without a reasonable doubt that he himself is surely sure about what he promises. When a man says, I love you to a woman, though he may be sincere and his intentions pure, the source of his love is not a sure thing, because he has yet to be faced with the challenge of loving "The One." Mrs. Destiny, like most women, has, in her past, the brutal testimony of her broken-heartedness talking over the innocence of her little girl hiding within. This is the little girl that used to prepare in anxious anticipation for love's coming. After multiple encounters with imposters, who used the language of love to arouse the beast of a freak God never intended to be awakened until the right time, the little girl, once convinced to believe in love and the promise that it gives, has had her pretty little butterfly wings clipped by those fraudulent checks she received and attempted to cash from her former bankrupt lovers. Due to the insufficient funds of love under the spell of a mysoginistically old regime of management, Mrs. Destiny chooses now only to believe in the kind of behaviors that confirm love as genuine rather than by the premature utterance of love's unchallenged proclamations void of the all credible reference capable of validating it as an authenticated extension from the origin of love's source. To whatever objective love is extended that objective will always challenge it to see if it embodies the character of love at the core of its nature. Women, no matter their ethnicity, religious preference, sexual orientation, size, or shape the desire for love, when it comes explaining what it is to back up the integrity of the word it spoke with actions that reveal the natural responses of the character it claims, is powerful. It is not until every man and women desiring to love or to experience love within the framework of the originators actual design that the natural order of love can be understood as an obtainable reality in the exploratory relationships.

God is the originator, the framework, and the actual design of love. The only time in this life when humanity achieves perfection is when it as a whole decides to love everyone the same way He loved and continues to love us. Hey Fellas, Scriptures warn us to love our wives as Christ loved the church! Christ showed love in action at the core of its natural response. Christ did not try to love the church; He just did, because it was natural for Him.

Most relationships fail today because partners try to love, without ever understanding that love is a natural part of God's nature. Anything outside of God's love is unnatural. For instance, if naturally, under the framework of God's design, He created you as a woman, then you do not have to try and be what you were naturally created to be. If God has blessed you with a gift to play a sport, sing, dance, or write, even though you have to work hard at it, you do not have to try and do it because for you doing it is like second nature. It is here that I must interject for the single, married, lonely, looking, waiting to be found, and all the in between relationship Ladies. The reason many have tried to love you and failed is because God has placed the nature of His love for you in a man He created, possessed with the fortitude, will, patience, resources and resolve to love you the way you need to be loved, naturally. Everybody else may have sincerely tried but because of the absence of God's love for you, not gently rest upon their heart, loving you for them, was wrong, even if they wanted it to be right.

Listen ladies, for every man that tried to love you, but because he loved GIRLS, GIRLS, GIRLS, GIRLS so much more, causing the nature of love to become unnatural, for each of them, I apologize. Please remember that a man was never created or intended to be the original source of love's inspiration, but a conduit God created through which He intended for love to express itself causing all attracted by it to become the natural reflection of its original source. It is simple, if God, the original source of love, is not the foundation of you and your significant other's relationship, then the love you claim to have for one another is unnatural and will eventually leave you painfully singing songs asking, *"What's love got to do with it?"*

Romantic relationships that adhere to the following blueprint of God's design will epitomize the action of love at the core of its nature 100 percent of the time: First, solidify the foundation of love in your own life by establishing a healthy love life with God. This will set the most reliable standard of love's nature upon which all unchallenged proclamations of love can be truthfully measured. After sorting through multiple applications determining only one candidate to be the right ONE for the job, slowly introduce this individual to the love relationship you have already established with the love of your life, God. See, you have to let them know up front that you love God? Though they may confidently say yes to their ability to stand up under the responsibilities of the job requirements, every woman must carefully watch to see if loving you for them is not work, but a privilege, natural. Remember love can only be natural when the vessel it is working through to reach you is connected to the same source you use as your measure. This is why two people desiring to join forces to become one should never seek to pull God into a relationship they have already established with one another before ever establishing a healthy love relationship with God first. They should rather first pull their significant other into an already established relationship with God, in order to secure God as their Rock, and the undisputable champion resting on the throne of their love foundation.

Like an adventurous explorer sailing out on the ferociously untamed seas eager to be the first to stake a claim on what is presumed to be unchartered territory, the Superhero Lover, after excitedly conquering a piece of land in the new world, under further examination of its condition begins to doubt, questioning if he really is the first or should he look to see how many others claimed it before him. With no evidence to support his doubts, ignited by a series of twenty-one unexpected questions, he responds, like a man that got knocked down, tried to get up quickly while stumbling attempting to re-establish his balance. Mustering up as much confidence as he could, hoping to dismiss the notion from his mind that his wife may feel like marrying him was a mistake, he declares like Usher *"If it's a question of my love, babe you got it."* Like most men, who most often misunderstand or feel inadequate when it comes to honoring those demands manifested through their significant others love language, the Superhero soulfully plagiarizes a line from a Tony Toni Tone song, doing his best impression of Milli Vanilli singing to his lovely, but presumably insecure lover, *"What makes you think that I would try to run game on you."*

With, Mrs. Destiny seeing her boo's unpreparedness for this big boy/big girl conversation she makes a ladylike maneuver, shifting the momentum back into the favor of love, by asserting her authority in their bed, banging down her booty, I mean her gavel, bringing order into the court of her bedroom. For the remainder of their honeymoon stay, she put her sweet thing on him, letting him know that at the moment she was the judge and when she comes into the room he better rise up because court is in session! In the words of Tye Tribbett, *"She turned it on him!"* Women have a magical way of opening up a man's heart, showing him what it really looks like and closing it back up all while erasing the procedure from his memory, like it never happened. After all, that was said, the doubts and questions that were still yet to be answered, Mrs. Destiny suppressed her concern of uncertainty about the future by making the most of a moment that would become a lasting memory they will need to reflect back on in the hard times of marriage. She made every night a night that allowed him to forget about all she said and only focus on the beauty of making love. She laid it on him so good that he could only think of her on two occasions, all day and all night.

As their Hawaiian feast for lovers comes to an end, and they journey back to the unknown of life on the other side of the honeymoon called marriage, they, like most naive newlyweds, arrive back home still under the spell of the honeymoon fever. With the reality of marriage, not quite yet having set in, both parties are eager to answer all the email, phone, and Facebook messages left by friends, family, and fans. The Superhero calls up his homie, who does not pick up the phone and leaves the following detailed message with the instrumental of Chris Brown's *These Girls Ain't Loyal* playing in the background on his homie's voice mail:

"Now what I'm about to say we need to keep between us two, if I hear her speak a word of this

to me then I know it came straight from you. Now listen she told me she was pleased but not satisfied, which caused me to ask why now at this time did we need to preoccupy ourselves with this bottom line? She proceeded, answering with a response that left me shook like a half way crook, scared to death, scared to look for her to look at my face unsure about how to respond. I am still shook. For a minute or two, I felt like she had flipped the script, pulled a Ralph Tresvant on me, and was trying to do what she had to do and break my heart.

Just at that moment, the singing anointing of Miguel came up on me, and I serenaded her with a little "Lotus Flower Bomb." I sang that song so good I almost made her believe I was Miguel. I sounded just like him! After that, she could not keep her hands off me. I had her body calling for me, and I came quickly to rescue my damsel from her distress. In the words of Lionel Richie, man "we did it all night long" and it was outstanding. She put it on me, blew my mind and my back out! After she started riding me, I grabbed her hair and pulled her track out. Now I know that I am the man, and I was supposed to tame her kitty cat, but man, she put it on me. She had me sucking on my thumb asking where my momma was at. Man, she's Fine, better than all the others I left behind. She stimulated my intellect, quieted my soul, and mesmerized my mind. While all at the same, I just have to say this, and I cannot lie, I thought that I was going to blow hers.

Honestly, if I had, to tell the truth, I confess, my sexy and vivacious Mrs. Destiny Lover, YOU BLEW MY MIND, BABE AND I AM SATISFIED!

Worthy of My Submission Or Should I Look for Another!

Session 3

"For it was thus that the pious women of old who hoped in God were [accustomed] to beautify themselves and were submissive to their husbands [adapting themselves to them as themselves secondary and dependent upon them]. It was thus that Sarah obeyed Abraham [following his guidance and acknowledging his leadership over her by] calling him lord (master, leader, authority)"
(1 Peter 3:5-6 AMP).

"We Made It!" the two overly consummated lovers happily exclaim as their plane touched down in the state where they will officially begin to explore the sometimes amazing and at other times horrific realities of marriage. As they exit off the plane, expecting to be swarmed by friends, family, fans and reporters, whom prior to their wedding were obsessed with their love story, Mr. and Mrs. Lover excitedly rush down the exiting walkway and up the escalator, jumping off it with a loud shout of "surprise," only to be greeted by a crowd of nobody. No, not one friend, fan, reporter, former flame, or stalker cared enough to show up to the couple's scheduled red carpet, *"I'm Coming Home"* celebration. Anticipating that their arrival would generate a greater turn out than LeBron James' heavily televised welcomed return to Cleveland, to their surprise, they were going to quickly have to learn how to play this game together in a stadium full of empty seats. Looking around, almost in disbelief, the two concluding that nobody was there nor was anybody coming they turn and stare at one another, realizing for the first time that really, "It's just me and you." They laughing, acting like this feeling they feel at the moment is not unusual, move over to the baggage claim, where they stand waiting for somebody to come and retrieve their luggage for them. After a few minutes, the naive newlyweds awaken out of their fantasy into the real time reality of "It's just the two us!" With only their hands and shoulders to count on, they reluctantly gather up their bags and start on their way to the house, which they will try to make their home.

Now with the honeymoon phase of their marital bliss, still fresh but gradually becoming less and less of an indescribable inspiration used to fuel their fire, they make a sharp turn down a one-way street called transition taking the first of their many steps into a lonely valley called the reality of matrimony. These two lovers, thriving off the adrenaline from their two-week enigmatically toasty and extremely sexual escapade, glowing like Leroy and Sho Nuff right before and during their Who is the Master battle in the Last Dragon, leap with joy, intensely looking for a somewhat secluded location to get their freak on. It was the one and only thing they knew at that time they could do to turn their frowns upside down.

At the ecstasy stage of honeymooners' hypnosis, the difficulty of transition slips under the radar of the human conscious, overshadowed by those uncontrolled emotions highly responsive to the urges of sexual stimuli. In other words, in the early stages of what can be called the honeymooner's delight, sex was the cure all and the way of escape they relied on to soften the pain of transitioning through those inevitable valley low and mountain high challenges that show up in every marriage. By definition, transition is the movement between two points in which power is released, and a deeper depth of revelation knowledge is given to enlighten the eyes of our understanding with regard to a pattern of movement previously taken by God. It is not discovering for the first time a partner you never knew before, but the rediscovering of a partner God saw fit to previously acquaint you with before your conception. It is the change or adjusting from one state, stage, condition, or place to another. More simply, it is the time spent in between two dimensions of destiny to help us understand the ordered steps of a road God has already walked us down before.

Just like a romantic love story, eloquently composed with the inked blood of God's pen, written with a host of key words that smoothly transition listeners through various phases of its blueprint in order for them to successfully comprehend with integrity God's intended message, every couple married or dating must learn how to hear from God in order to make the necessary adjustments to achieve not their will, but God's will for their coming together. God is a life coach who masterfully recruits players with the right skills and attitude to play on a dream team with a roster of only two individuals capable of bringing the best out of each other. For any team to be successful, in marriage, the players must always be ready and willing to make the necessary adjustments according to their coaches' observation, because when the team fails, it is not the players that get the most criticism, but the coach for the weakness of a strategy he guaranteed would reward the team success.

Marriage is God's perfect system created with two distinctly different offices to be occupied by two imperfect people that choose to play together on the same team, under the leadership of the greatest championship winning coach of all time, G-O-D! So then, the questions that must be asked are, what team are you playing for and who is your head coach? Do you think you or the other player on your team need to be traded or do the two of you just need to be whipped into perfect condition under the guidance a coach that can make the necessary adjustments that will propel your team into the Hall of Fame under the prestigious title of Greater than all the Rest?

As time passes from one year married to two years married to three years married, Mr. and Mrs. Lover, having totally exited out of the honeymoon phase of marriage, and entered nervously into the second stage of marriage called the reality or adjustment phase. They questioning their ability to stand up under pressures that will follow, now that play time is over, and the business reality of marriage is set to begin, hope the pleasures of their experience thus far will incite the both of them to work together because they want to, rather than out of forced obligation. As a result, they question if whether or not they are compatible with one another and their coaches requested adjustments all because of their differences of opinions on what their roles on the team are supposed to be.

Dancing to the awkward rhythm of two hearts once beating at the same rate, now pulsating at dangerously abnormal speeds, they attempt to move with precision as if to suggest they were a united force only to stumble over the question of who would be a better lead and why God intended for the other to follow their leading. Interestingly enough the Superhero Lover begins to explain why he should be the lead in their dirty dancing routine stating, "I am your husband, and you need to follow my lead because God said so in His Word. I am the King of this castle and yes you are my Queen, but the Word says you need to listen to me, do what I say, submit to my authority, and honor me as your lord." With that said, the Sexy, Vivacious and Classy Mrs. Destiny responds to this exaggerated Scriptural interpretation of her supposed king to whom she just found out she was supposed to bow down to, by sarcastically singing in the seductively commanding voice of Beyoncé, *"Before you, it was just me, myself, and I boo."* She, following her solo with the low blow male castrating question, asks: Honestly, I am not even sure if you are worthy of my submission, causing me to question if I should look to be found by another who is?

With the ring of the bell, the third round of this ever evolving story ends with both lovers heading to their individual corners to calm their nerves and to figure out a better way to counter the impact of their spouse's blows. The Superhero Lover's corner cautions its angry lover to be careful of what he asked for because submission poses a higher level of difficulty on him than it does on her. Mrs. Destiny's corner, although pleased with her counter punches, which created some distance between the two lovers, informs her that her comments were recklessly uncalculated and that she must soften her heart to submit to his lead because he is the man she counted worthy of appreciating the value of her worth.

So, just what is the correct view of submission from both a man and woman's vantage point? Submission is the relinquishing (giving up) by choice of a woman's right to provide for herself, over to the sufficiency of the one blessed with the nature, will, resources, and appreciation of her worth—a God-man dedicated to meeting every one of her mandatory needs and all her wants without the over exertion of her efforts. A woman's submission is not the subservient surrender of her rights over to the rulership of a master, but rather her acknowledgment of a man worthy, capable, and responsible enough to provide for her, not because she cannot provide for herself, but out of appreciation for her presence. His desire is to make sure she never wants for anything he can readily accommodate her with. If women truly understood their power in submission, they would more likely side with a stance that supports the posture of God's position on this subject.

Submission in my estimation, when understood correctly, is harder for the man found worthy of it than for the woman committing her wellbeing over to this man's trust. A husband must be capable of providing at least at the same or above the level of his wife's father's provision, in order to ease the pain of transitioning under the authority of his leadership.

Because God has marked the man as the head of the family, He holds him primarily accountable for its institution. Ladies, if he is faithfully following God, not perfect but following God, with the highest consideration of your need to exist in the framework of God's plan for your life together, then let him lead. Remember, leaders carry on their shoulders the weight and the burden of those that follow.

Ladies, think about when you are in need or want for anything. I know you can get it yourself because you are independent, but when you are submitted to the one God crowned as worthy, you have a right to place a demand for what you want on the shoulders of your husband, making him responsible for meeting your desired expectation. This is called working smarter rather than harder. In no way am I saying women cannot lead, but only that God has determined the husband to be the leader of the family. Husbands must never seek to dominate from the posture of a dictator but seek to provide the highest elevation of love as a servant leader.

Like a server at a restaurant, a husband is supposed to provide the most exceptional customer service for his wife, who should be his number one customer, to ensure her continued interest in his business. He is supposed to bless her with the kind of service that always causes her to leave him with a little extra when she tips, even when she does not have it within herself to give. For every husband, what I just said might have gone over your head, so let me make it clear. If you bless your wife, then she will always be ready to give you her best, even when she does not feel her best, just because you have been so, so good! Honestly, the beauty of submission can only be seen when both the recipient and the submissively surrendered become selfless, taking more thought in caring for one another, so that neither will have the time to think more highly than they ought to think about themselves.

Although it has been said that a husband and wife should not go to bed angry, but rather stay up all night if necessary to come together, after cooling down of course, to peacefully resolve an issue that has been intensely disputed, this undocumented law can be found in a book written by someone probably not married; both Mr. and Mrs. Lover declare that as for our house we sure as hell will not be having this discussion tonight. As they head back toward their individual locker rooms, both bleeding and nursing the wounds from their Who's the Master fiasco, they, in the heat of the moment, yell out some hurtful words to get under each other's skin, setting the scene for the time when they will meet again.

Like the mystery centered around a Rick Flare and Dusty Rhodes NWA title fight, each of the two distraught lovers heap to themselves teachers that agree with what their itching ears want to hear, venting to their entourages (friends, family, colleagues, sometimes former flames) who even after they kiss and make up, stay mad and always ready to fight all because of their lack of discretion. The next morning, the Superhero Lover with the legendary Flick Flare, "Whoo" struts across the bedroom floor making his way to the bathroom doing his best expression of the nature boy Rick Flare pimp walk, implying to Mrs. Destiny, who is still lying in the in the bed naked, pretending to be asleep, with her body seductively postured in one of his more favorable positions, that he does not give a care about what she had to say about him last night. After handling his morning business, he, exiting out of the bathroom on the way back to his locker room, is unexpectedly surprised by Mrs. Destiny's sudden change in behavior as she lay in the bed with heels on, her arms held high and thighs spread wide hoping to make things all better with her Mandingo by enticing him with her well-proportioned extremities pulsating to the soulfully freaky sound of Ciara's *Body Parts*." Forgetting those things which are behind, and reaching forth unto those things which are before, they press towards a mark set by the Apostle Paul, through the power of concession, made in Corinthians clearly stating for each of the two marital occupants to always desire to do the due with one another, even when their emotions violently protest against their reunion:

"But since sexual immorality is occurring, each man should have sexual relations with his own wife, and each woman with her own husband. The husband should fulfill his marital duty to his wife, and likewise the wife to her husband. The wife does not have authority over her own body but yields it to her husband. In the same way, the husband does not have authority over his own body but yields it to his wife. DO NOT DEPRIVE EACH OTHER EXCEPT BY MUTUAL CONSENT AND FOR A TIME, SO THAT YOU MAY DEVOTE YOURSELVES TO PRAYER. THEN COME TOGETHER AGAIN SO THAT SATAN WILL NOT TEMPT YOU BECAUSE OF YOUR LACK OF SELF-CONTROL" (1 Corinthians 7:3-5).

Mrs. Destiny fully cognizant of how her show of due benevolence would cause her stubborn Mr. Lover Man with no resistance to surrender voluntarily after being ambushed by the seduction of her good kisser and the oil dripping all on the crest of her bosom down onto the extremities of all her other assets, refuses to deprive herself or her babe from what they both need and want, eliminating the need to look for love anywhere else when there is more than enough of it at home. No, Ms. Toni Braxton, Love should not have had to bring him home last night, but real love rests easy because it knows he will surely return home early to a house where love always satisfies. So Mrs. Destiny put it down, laid it on him real good. She did what he never ever thought that she would. With her black panties wet, moist like a piece of cake, whispering in the Superhero Lover's ear, "Can't wait for you to do it until my legs shake." See, she will not keep her good loving from her man. She knows if she feeds a dog when he is hungry, he will not have the time to sniff for hoes. Because he knows these hoes are not royal, he sees no need to depend on them, because he knows his wife is loyal. You may or may not like this song, but to every wife give love to your man whether he is right and even more so when he is wrong. You have all the control in your hands; submission to your husband truly is a part of God's plan. So let me make this point, and let me make it clear, you need to open up your eyes and your ears because this is something that you need to hear. For all the married and those aspiring to be married, I humbly urge and strongly suggest that if you intend to excel to the highest pinnacle of marital success, never leave your spouse with what is left of you after giving to all of the rest, acting like your reserve is better than your better and best. Protect your investment, avoid temptation, and observe the sexual areas where your spouse struggles to master the content you the teacher let them know would be on the test. So then, you can tutor and teach them how to master the art of making love accompanied by the freakiness of an indescribable and so amazingly healthy life of sex.

Yes, the two Lovers experienced their first of many more break up just to make up love sessions. After the first session ended they concluded that maybe they needed to disagree with one another more often so that they could sit down again at the table, sup together, wear out, dust off, he unclog her hole, and she drain his pipe that almost blocked their love, sex, and holy matrimonial reunion from being what it was supposed to be under the conditions of their original agreement. Like Michael Jackson's *Off the Wall* Album, you, if married, in the early years of being newlyweds, learned how to groove and let the madness in music get to you and just enjoy yourself with the full fill of all your nastiest sexual fantasies. But after the love is gone and the sex that used to be right, still good but becomes old, stale, and wrong, then what? What then, when your girl that use to remind you of your jeep when you wanted to ride it, starts to break down and malfunction due to all the high mileage you put on her begins to break down as a result of low maintenance and your reckless driving?

After the Superhero Lover's exaggerated serenading of *"Sex me babe"* to his destined lover becomes an old played out sexual prerequisite for dismissing a trial they face, how then will they handle the difficulty of marriage long after the passion of sex leaves them numb, no longer a suitable form of medication for an unhealed couples inflicted wounds? Is there not more to a loving relationship than sex? So then, after the sex is gone, then just what comes next?

After Sex Then What?

Session 4

But if they have not self-control (restraint of their passions), they should marry. For it is better to marry than to be aflame [with passion and tortured continually with ungratified desire] (1 Corinthians 7:8 AMP).

As the dawn of a new day breaks through the barriers of the night sky, riding in on the timed wave of the sun's rise, the excitement advertised in Jet, Ebony, and some of the other more formidable marital advice magazines regarding the unexplored wonders of another day's married possibility, is insulted by the extremely low expectation gesture that wakes up on the wrong side of the bed yelling out, "It's the same bull.....ish, just another day!" So just how in seven years of marriage could the two love birds who, at first glance, appeared to be inseparable, be hanging more steadily on the side of "YES" when asking themselves the question, "Did I Miss God?"

As the Superhero rises, the same as he does every morning, anxious to roll over into the arms of his sleeping beauty, he instead is greeted by some Lady that looks like a dude sleeping in his bed and messing with his head.

"Young man, who in the hell are you? What are you doing in my bed and what did you do with the woman who was laying here beside me, my wife?" Then all of a sudden he hears, "Babe it's me; it's me; it's me, your sexy and vivacious Mrs. Destiny, your queen, your bride. Babe, it is me!" He, frightened by the dainty still soft spoken voice of what he thinks sounds like his babe, but has a body like Fiona in *Shrek*, not the princes but Fiona in her more ogerly form does a double take just to see whether this thing was real or another nightmare on Elm Street. Ahhhhhhhhhhhhh! Trying to wake up out of what he was hoping was a dream, he screaming, "It can't be! Babe, is that really you?" leaps quickly off the spread from where they lay guessing at who this somebody is that was sleeping in his bed, this somebody that has unwelcomingly taken his babe's place.

Upon a more thorough investigation of the suspect, the Superhero Lover rescinded the missing person all-points bulletin he released prematurely, once he realized this so called imposter was telling the truth. After a few times of him looking at her now and a picture of her back when they first got together, he like Boys II Men, fell down on bending knees crying out "Why?" hoping to discover an answer to explain the dilemma he now is wondering how he got himself into. Since there are, however, always two sides to every story, I can only image what it would be like if we had the chance to probe the thoughts gently resting on the abnormally active brain cells of his better half. Those explicit thoughts we might be able to carefully observe on the projected big screen of her first motion picture capturing the unsettling of her feelings towards the Superhero Lover, then and now. Just what might we find in the eyes of this Superhero Lover's sweet thing when she rolls over and realizes that what it is now is not becoming of what she thought it was supposed to be?

As she woke up this morning, Jill Scotting it to the rhythmic sound of the summer rain drops rubbing against the exterior of her bay window frame, trickling down the four corners of their fortified layer, she anxious to snuggle up with her Mr. Everything upon rolling over instead is greeted by mister, mister wrong. Expecting to break out into a glisten after beholding what she just knew she would be unable to resist, she sweating profusely and staring at him like "eeelllllllll" singing to him in the words of Angela Bofill, "I tried to do the very best I could for you, but it's still not enough," levitates off the bed like a woman scorned. Laying there looking like Harpo from the Color Purple, Mrs. Destiny extends the Mrs. Celie two-finger E.T. peace sign over her low down dirty shame of a man, chanting while he slept, "Until you do right by me, everything you do is going to fail." Damn, Damn, Damn, she yells out like Florida Evans on *Good Times* after coming to realize from the looks of things that times are not so good.

Those raindrops she thought she heard rubbing against the exterior of her bay windows were only gun shots busting out car windshields next to her obscured view of the only bay she could see looking out of her window, Pelican Bay State Prison. That trickling down of water from the four corners of their fortified layer was the continuous leak of a busted water pipe they were unable to fix due to economic hardship, streaming down the walls onto the foundation of their 700 square foot, one bedroom, no bath, mold ridden, rented shack of a mansion. "You said you would take me away from the pain and bring me to paradise, but Negro, please! You are a pain in the (bleep), and you have brought me nothing but disappointment. Please do not get me started on the so-called paradise you were supposed to bring me because living with you is like living in hell, you stingy-hearted midget of a man! I should have listened to my father; he was right; YOU REALLY ARE NOT WORTHY OF ME!"

It is funny how the emotional explosion, taking place within the mind of the two sides parallel above, over the course of time, has managed to create in the both of them the fear of an obstacle they will only be able to breakthrough when they learn how to respect each other individually and corporately during those silent conversations they have with themselves about the other. Those kinds of conversations that are silent enough for only one to hear, but loud enough for the spouse over which the dialogue is being spoken to see the working of the other's inner Lucious and/or Cookie stabbing them in the back because of those overlooked insecurities that have deceitfully convinced their betrayer to believe they should be the sole heir sitting at the head seat of their Empire. For this reason, both Mr. and Mrs. Lover's monologues have been unfolded for you to expose the differences in how they prioritize their cares, concerns, and expectations for their life long relationship.

It is clear the Superhero Lover, like most men, has ranked at the top of his list of non-negotiables that Mrs. Destiny must always make it her priority to be and stay ready with the sexy at all times. The phrase 'to be and stay ready with the sexy' is the disciplined posture of any wife determined to remain relevant in the eyes of her husband who delights in her ability always to be sexy, a Seductively Educated X something, now the bodacious young hot mama wife of a worthy suitor, no matter the circumstance of life. This is a woman that makes no excuses, but who is somehow amazingly able to turn what little she has into a whole lot. She is the kind of wife that whenever it is time to hold him down or whenever it is time to give it up, she, without any hesitation, surrenders all of her body to him, giving everything to him, withholding nothing. For thousands of years, men have searched all over but could not find nobody, looked high and low, been around the world and I, I, they still cannot find this flawless perfection of the female species, because she is the epitome of an idea that just does not exist.

Just like those two nerdy teenagers in the 1985 hit movie, *Weird Science*, who successfully created their fantasy dream woman on a computer, the Superhero Lover's delusions of grandeur have caused him to become overwhelmed with the elusive ideal of a woman's worth, without taking any account for all her imperfections. See, sometimes we men tend to allow all a woman's curves and all her edges to blind us to the reality of all her perfect imperfections. It is when these Lovers become comfortably reacquainted with one another, as their relationship progresses over time, that she introduces the rest of, in the words of John Legend, her All of Me individual, the person he did not realize at the time he was saying "Yes" to.

Now with her natural and unnatural patterns of behavior, she was too embarrassed to share in the early stages of their relay, redefining an acceptable standard by which the Superhero Lover assumed all women were supposed to live, Mrs. Destiny, with no care or regard for the unofficial female creed of don't ask, don't tell, and don't show then he won't know, has exposed all the unknowns of her journey through the once-secret society of the female fraternal order. Ladies, there is no need to show and tell Mr. Right about all the explicit details of your body change, but like Job, for all the days of your struggle, please wait until your change comes. Honestly Ladies, there are some things you can keep between you and God! Things like passing gas, acting like it was not you, and leaving the room so, so, so Funkdafied! Or telling him you are on your period and leaving evidence at the scene of the bloody crime for him to add to his mental file. What about always telling him you are bloated, have gas, or have to go to the bathroom? He does not care. Just do it and do it with discretion. Also, when you know he needs some real good loving, but he is troubled by what he sees, stop and take a look at yourself. You have the nerve to get in the bed with the Arabian Sikh Turban wrapped around your head, looking like Bin Laden's twin sister, those 1980 Magic Johnson sweat socks, rocking them like LL in the 90's with one up one down, the ugly shirt he asked you to throw away with the bleach spots on it, and truly the worst of all, those big mama bloody Sunday period panty draws you wear, constantly reminding him that you are a woman with a friend that sticks with you closer than a brother. Though for the most part some of the issues mentioned above are natural inclinations all women go through, the regularity of the frequency with which she continues to show recklessly and tell is her way of saying to her love that sexy is on vacation, not quite sure when she is coming back, so let me introduce you to the woman behind the mask, the real me.

So just who is this sexy, absent the flamboyant demonstration that accommodates the fame associated with her stage name? Mr. Lover, who expects his wife to always be pole ready, just like a stripper, and like most men who foolishly believe they should always and forever be the center of attention for their wife's sexy stripper performance, becomes more elated by the motion of her smoothly sliding her body up and down on that pole, I mean up and down, that he underestimates the far exceeding value of the women she is off stage. The evolution of her Seductively Educated X something into the bodacious Young hot mama wife of a supposed worthy suitor, is determined by the security, safety, and applause for Mrs. Destiny's off stage personality to whom the Superhero Lover is supposed to be just a junkie for her love. See, a wife feels comfortable releasing the hostage of her sexy inner stripper over to the proper authority negotiating with her off-stage personality for her unharmed escape, only when her perpetrator committing this unlawful crime, finds a safely secured location where both parties involved can be appreciated and able to freely voice their feelings without any criticism. Mrs. Destiny's sex shooter, shooting love in the Superhero Lover's direction, like anyone ever held hostage, desires to be rescued from her harbored insecurities and chaperoned into a place safe enough to secure the weight of her blemished past, the miracle of her present, and the promise of her future all at the same time.

If then, Mrs. Destiny is not living up to the acceptable standard the Superhero Lover assumed all women were supposed to live by, could that be because the proper authority, that ensured her safety, over to whom she willing released herself has not properly secured her into a witness protection program? Has the Superhero Lover provided both her sexy and her off stage personality with the sufficiency of a well-trained security detail that makes her without question know she is secured? The question then is, is Mr. Lover only providing for her with a light drizzle in her drought season and if so, is it even possible for him to turn up and make it, make it rain to ensure a welcomed harvest into her vineyard?

After New Edition, in 1990, called for the interrogation of every so-called ride or die chick through the soulful sound of *"Can You Stand the Rain,"* to stand by their man no matter what, the integrity with which the question was asked begin to shift in favor of all women who in response declared that every man could make it rain, but in what way does he shower down rain on me? When it rains, does it always show in the form of a ferocious storm with Category 5 hurricane like winds or like the beauty of summer raindrops falling to the ground, each tapping rhythmically to the melodious beat of a wonderfully composed Carl Thomas classic? Yes, storms will come; this we know for sure. However, storms should never outweigh the cool of the day that comes after the outpouring of a timely summer rain shower. Most showers are caused by the natural lowering and accelerating of temperatures in the atmosphere that determine, for all couples, their daily weather conditions. As a result, of the projected forecast, the necessary accommodation can now be made ahead of time to ensure each party will be dressed appropriately in order for the both of them to continue to function normally, no matter the intensity of the storm.

Yes, it is true, storms move things that need to be moved, and sometimes things that God intended to stay. A relationship filled with nothing but the continuous soaking of a never-ending storm will only pull people that God willed to be together further apart, without the illuminating glow of a colorful rainbow validating the reviving glory of a summer rain. After the unbearable heat usually associated with a scorching hot summer day, the comfort of a soothing summer rain is like the quenched fire of a desired fantasy fulfilled. Storms are unexpected, but the summer rain is the desired outpouring of relief from the sweltering heat from an expected shower. Like any wife after listening intently for the sound of abundant rain that would make the holy ground on which she stands fertile and ready to produce through the pores of her DNA, Mrs. Destiny sings within herself, "Not only are you going to respect me, but YOU GONNA LOVE MEEEEEEEEEEEEEE!"

The skill and precision with which every woman expects to be loved are learned through the voluntary surrender of the man submitted under a teacher committed to answering his request of "please, teach me how to love you." Even though it is dually noted that there are many highly qualified certified teachers in the game today, a certificate only grants one, legally, with the credentials to teach, but not necessarily the wisdom needed to make the correct adjustments to accommodate the learning level of her student. I, therefore, declare that no man can love a woman right until she is willing to teach him how to love her and he willingly commits to excelling above the requirements outlined on the recommended syllabus for her class. Women, you are the certified educators commissioned to teach the man God has anointed for you how to love you the way you need to be loved. Unfortunately, like most educators, women eventually come to find out that God is not only an overly protective parent when it comes to the education of the student, but He also requires the teachers He hired for the job to teach their student how to love from the standards identified in His Kingdom curriculum. This, however, can be a lot more challenging, because when it comes to how to love a woman, most men, have a learning disability.

Many men display towards their destined lover symptoms associated with learning handicaps more commonly referred to as ADHD, dyslexia, and autism. Men are ADHD because staying focused long enough on the needs of someone other than themselves is a difficult task; dyslexic because men have a hard time reading, responding, and connecting with the pulse of their significant other's love language. Lastly, men at times show signs of autism through their impaired ability to effectively communicate and interact, verbally and non-verbally, with the kind of gestures that dance to the tune of their woman's worth. Ladies, surely you did not think teaching a man how to love was going to be easy! If you did not know, now you know that just like pimpin, teaching ain't easy! Teaching is especially not easy if the one teaching has failed to master for herself the content she expects her student lover to so very easily apprehend. Is it even possible for Mrs. Destiny to teach the Superhero Lover how to love the person she is still trying to find out how to love herself?

With her destined lover's changed outlook on her beauty that he used to boast about how blessed he was to behold, now seeming to suddenly be wiped clean from the memories loaded on his disk drive, Mrs. Destiny is placed in the uncomfortable position of recovering the love files lost due to the illegal hacking of her lover's server. Even with the difficulty of a task she willfully said yes to, Mrs. Destiny, while searching for the sense of security she hoped would be automatically awarded for her without the concern for how it would be provided, has to find the peace that passes all understanding in her relationship with Mr. Lover even while he shows little to no regard for her safety.

Interestingly enough, even with all the ammunition and firepower she could use to her advantage, announcing publically the character flaws of the Superhero Lover, she despite his openly harsh criticism of her, refuses to succumb to the same shameful tactics usually applied in an attempt to force a person to change. Like the beauty of a godly woman's resolve she could at any time have loudly announced for all to hear about the shortcomings of love, but instead moves gracefully possessed with the captivating allure that makes her man and every man stand up when she walks by chanting, "She's a lady oh, oh, oh she's a lady!" She is a Lady because the confidence of her swagger is ignited from within without the approval of outsiders. Like a tree planted by the river, whose roots always blessed with a sufficient supply from the streaming water beside which it stands, never having to depend on any external factors for it to remain secure in its position, Mrs. Destiny is a lady with an earned PhD in the science of learning how to love one's self. For every wife or women aspiring to be married, please remember never to neglect the responsibility of taking care of your vineyard.

In the Song of Solomon, the first chapter, midway down the sixth verse, the queen declares, "My mother's children were angry with me; they made me the keeper of the vineyards: *but mine own vineyard have I not kept"* (Song of Solomon 1:6 (KJV)).

Self-preservation is the first law of nature that reminds us that our vineyard should never be neglected. Your vineyard is the inherited field bursting with the sweet smelling aroma of fermented grapes peeled from the demanding inventory of your well-kept harvested grapevines, used to produce the highest quality of wine, leaving you legally intoxicated in the beauty of your Father's created glory. Scriptures tell us, *"He (man) is the image and glory of God: but the woman is the glory of the man."* The poise and posture of a confident God are reflected in a man. The word glory in the Hebrew is "KABOD" and it means "weight" or heaviness. In other words, God knows that He can lean on a man and trust that he will be able to stand upright under the weight or heaviness of His honor while holding Him up.

Likewise, Mrs. Destiny, for most superheroes, is that safe place all husbands like to lean on. Like the virtuous woman in Proverbs 31, who perceives that her merchandise is good: and her candle goes not out by night, Mrs. Destiny's life is a wifely journaling for every woman in a relationship to understand that the only way her Superhero Lover will be able to delight in the rich taste of her wine, produced from the vines of her beautiful vineyard, is when she decides to be the first partaker of what she has graciously offered to him. Simply put, if she does not enjoy walking in her own garden, then how can she teach him how to do something she cannot do herself? If she does not know who she is then how can she teach him how to love someone she does not know herself? Every superhero desires to drink wine, drawn from the grapevines of their Ms. Destiny's vineyard. Yes, every husband should desire to drink that water from his wife's well that will cause him never to thirst again, but in order for this to happen she must always seek to advertise her intoxicating drink as a continuously evolving production from which he will one day benefit. So even when it seems like her well has run dry, he must never stop investing into her as his treasure. In Proverbs 5:15-20 the writer poetically states,

"Drink water from your own cistern, running water from your own well. Should your springs overflow in the streets, your streams of water in the public squares? Let them be yours alone, never to be shared with strangers. May your fountain be blessed, and may you rejoice in the wife of your youth. A loving doe, a graceful deer, may her breast satisfy you always, may you ever be intoxicated with her love."

For all my superhero lovers, the key is to cherish each day, whether good or bad. Allow her to rest in the assurance that your love, no matter, what will always be committed to the provision of her preservation. Just stay committed! When you love her or when you feel like choking the hell out of her, stay committed. Superheroes do not quit when the going gets tough; they find a way to persevere through the struggle and press their way to victory. Where are the real superheroes? We need some superheroes that are going to stand up and fight for their marriage and stop acting like wimps cheating on their wives with other women just because they got a big butt and smile. Stop drinking that poison; wake up and fight for the wife of your youth. Encourage her to see the queen she is, the queen you married and still expect her to become. This is the refining fire every marriage must go through in order to be molded into the idea of that threefold cord that is not easily broken. This is that consuming fire, sweet perfume, the awesome presence of lovers learning how to flow in their mellow, smooth groove.

As a result of their devotedness to God, gracing them with the staying power to remain together, the Superhero Lover and Ms. Destiny can now honestly declare that they have Been Through the Fire, Pushed To The Limit, With Their Backs to the Wall, but they made it. So then the only question still left to be answered at this point in their relationship is after the wounded heart and scars suffered from the third-degree burns on their journey together through the fire, is it possible for their love to be stronger than the pride of the pain? Yes, they made it, but how much more do they have left to give after they have come through the fire? What now after the fire?

Through the Fire!

Session 5

"Now if any man build upon this foundation gold, silver, precious stones, wood, hay, stubble; Every man's work shall be made manifest: for the day shall declare it, because it shall be revealed by fire; and the fire shall try every man's work of what sort it is. If any man's work shall abide which he hath built thereupon, he shall receive a reward. If any man's work shall be burned, he shall suffer loss; but he himself shall be saved; yet so as by the fire" (1 Corinthians 3:12-15).

"The First Time Ever- I – Saw - Your- Face," a classic off yes Ms. Roberta Flack's album entitled, *"First Take"* should make everyone of us in a relationship reflect, based on the lyrics of the song, back on the first time we were blessed to behold the beauty of love in the face of our destined lover. Yes, the true love face that causes a damsel's heart to flutter rapidly like the wings of a butterfly or like a young lad praising God

forcefully after rediscovering that love, all the while, was waiting for him to be found. No, when we first met that was not the first time. No, the first, second, third, or fourth date was not the first time. Not when we moved in together, when we slept together, and surely not on that special day when we naively said I do. Ladies, ladies no, it was not after the first time he smacked it up, flipped it, and rubbed it down to!

No, truly the first time The Superhero Lover and Mrs. Destiny, like most of us, ever saw their significant other's face was after they were pushed to the limit, with their backs pressed up against the wall, while coming right down through the fire. The fire, presumably the most avoided ingredient in all love relationships, is to be ranked the highest among all the non-negotiable relationship essentials. The fire is the inevitable reality that always comes to determine the quality of character and the authenticity of the substance upon which each of loves foundations is believed to be secured on.

"Now if any man build upon this foundation gold, silver, precious stones, wood, hay, stubble; Every man's work shall be made manifest: for the day shall declare it, because it shall be revealed by fire; and the fire shall try every man's work of what sort it is. If any man's work shall abide which he hath built thereupon, he shall receive a reward. If any man's work shall be burned, he shall suffer loss; but

he himself shall be saved; yet so as by the fire" (1 Corinthians 3:12-15, KJV).

So here they stand, on the other side of a raging fire that consumed the home where they still live, with some ferociously hot flames resting over their relationship, kissing the sky with a thick cloud of smoke. Interesting enough, in most house fires, bystanders usually call 9-1-1, and try to assist with the rescue of anyone that may still be left in the house. This was not so with Mr. and Mrs. Lover's Home! Unfortunately, when the roof of the Superhero Lover and Mrs. Destiny's house was on fire, the Daily Times most diabolical reporter stood across the way singing, "Burn Baby Burn" along with the backup vocals of all their haters chanting, "The Roof, the Roof, the Roof is on fire, We don't need no water let the ……………….. Burn!" The Superhero Lover and Mrs. Destiny, however, to the surprise of all their haters, escaped through the ruins of the fire with life-threatening wounds, barely standing but still alive. With a slight stutter and a puzzled look of disbelief, the Daily Times most diabolical reporter mischievously runs toward the Lovers expressing a posture of care and concern, thinking as he embraces the two of them, "How, how in, in, in the hell did they come through that fire alive? He, like the imposter he is, along with former flames still waiting for the Superhero Lover to come back to love, and those playa haters who refuse to turn their heads around act as if they are a part of the search and rescue team, seek not to ensure their safety, but to exaggerate the severity of the wounds suffered in their furnace of affliction in order to derail their confidence in the possibility of a full recovery.

Yes, it is all about their confidence! The confidence to believe that what each participant earlier in the relationship arrogantly declared their allegiance to, a declaration only validated through the action of standing and staying when the going gets tough, and the tough gets going, would be confirmed by a consistent demonstration of love acts. The confidence to stop speaking about what is not right in your relationship, but instead, speak about it what God said it is supposed to be, remaining still until your change comes, all while standing together under the blood-stained banner of life's insurmountable difficulties that come to test the durability of your foundation. This is the kind of confidence that only comes through a blood, sweat, and tears God inspired devotedness of a lady, yes a lady, mature enough to understand that tough times are a clarion call for her to put her big girl panties on, and for her fallen hero to continue to encourage her with Godly wisdom while she adjusts to walking in panties that are a few sizes bigger than her level of maturity. This kind of confidence only comes through the awe-inspiring tradition of a dedicated man who, despite the harsh, sometimes fair criticisms from his destined lover, and his acceptance of the distance between the image she projected on Facebook, in comparison with what he expects her to look like now, faithfully still stands by anxiously waiting for her to grow her wings and fly like the beautiful butterfly she is. This confidence causes a man to accept responsibility for not securing the launching pad for Mrs. Destiny, the foundation upon which their relationship was supposed to be built, and providing his love with the safety she needed for her life to boldly take off in a direction that would match up with her Godly expectation of where she projected she should be presently. The absence of this confidence, if not a natural ingredient abiding within the thoughts of each of the two personalities standing on the same foundation, will destroy the relationship because it has no depth in its grounding causing its roots to be scorched by the wildfire that swept through to challenge its allegiance. To whom, to what, or to where now, after having come through the fog of the fire, will their allegiance rest? Will they, despite their physical and emotional wounds, finally see each other's face and declare, "I'm a believer in the endurance of love and all that it promises to give?" Or will they show forth a disdain for one another, due to the fragility of their once perceived indestructible posture, passing the blame for the fire off on one another because of their ignorance of its origin and their inability to explain love's absences and its insufficiency?

The over exaggeration of love as the primary cause that makes relationships work has excused those who have pledged their allegiance to another in holy matrimony, from seeking after the applied knowledge that exposes all of love's impossibilities. In the words of the honorable Dr. Myles Munroe, "Love does not keep a marriage together, but a successful marriage hinges on the application of knowledge." The ignorance of the unlearned perishing, not only from a lack but from a blatant rejection of Godly knowledge regarding how to continue to mature together at a steady rate no matter the conditions, has caused Superhero lovers everywhere and their destiny lovers to throw in the towel and tap out prematurely all due to a lack of credible information: *My people are destroyed for a lack of knowledge: because thou hast rejected knowledge, I will reject thee"* (Hosea 3:6 KJV).

It is pivotal for the Superhero Lover and Mrs. Destiny at this point in their relationship to apply the knowledge of that stored up information; they naively thought they knew, to a forgotten but good old time classic tune called practicality. Mrs. Destiny's earlier question of how much do you love me, asked under the misguided assumption that love is the guarantee of successful relations, is immeasurable without first understanding the credibility of the information the Superhero Lover has chosen to love her with. So as they stand, beholding each other's face for the first time, after coming out of the fire, Mrs. Destiny shoots first, firing the shot heard around the world, asking him, "After this test by whose standard of knowledge are you expecting me to measure up to? Yours, everybody else's, or God's? Is your love for me based upon the high demand of your unrealistic expectation, the false witness testimony of your friends, yes how many of us really have them, or from the river of living water from which the origin of all knowledge continues to be revealed, God?

"When you speak the intensity of the tone in your voice, manipulated by the ego of those on the outside only familiar with your side of our story, echoes back to me the opinion of your mommy and many others. You see, I am not your momma, but I am your girl. I am the well-oiled muscled machine, that ride or die chick, the bricked upped house God built specifically for nobody but "YOU" endowed with the highest level of stamina to patiently bear with you until you and I can smile again. Please tell me, when will I see you smile again? Life has taken away your beautiful smile from me, and I want it back. Your pain has erased the credibility of your natural core and replaced it with a frustrated frown that implies to others that you are not happy.

Are you happy, with you, with me, with us? It is the answer to this question that stirs up within me an uneasy feeling of discomfort. My need, to ask, compels me to look back at some of my behaviors that may have unintentionally disrupted the flow of our joy. I see now that the zeal of being your wife along with the hunger and thirst for the knowledge of how to be it, has proven me to be one of the weak links in the chain that holds our marriage together. My secret insecurities and uncertainties caused all my well-intentioned thoughts about you and me to be obscured because I eclipsed you, the light of so many promising sunny days, with an idol called me.

I thought it was because of your negligence that our happy home had been consumed by the fire and I panicked when I realized I was being swallowed up in a struggle in which we both were drowning. You, I believed, if nobody else could, were supposed to be there to rescue me from the evil one and make me happy. More concerned with what everybody from the outside would think if they knew our struggle, I put on a happy face and disguised my disappointment with the fictitious response of, "Everything is fine" while trying to escape reality by denying the existence of its trouble. I spoke to you as my problem instead of as my champion and watched wave after wave swallow you up, never sincerely becoming for you that lifeline of support you needed to rescue you from drowning.

For all the things that I could have controlled in our relationship, but did not, I am sorry. I never gave my best to you, because I never thought my best would ever be enough. I thought I could make you happy, but you are not. Now, I understand that my job was never to make you happy, nor was it to withdraw from your happiness, but to add to the happiness you have already established within yourself. So what are you going to do? I really do not care about what everyone is going to say when they find out that we have problems! Babe in the words of Freddie Jackson, "I am your lady, I am everything you need and more! I am telling you I am not going anywhere. I am staying, and you are going to love me because I know for sure that you are the best man I have ever known.

The credibility of your references, however, playa is what will ultimately determine the legitimacy of your argument as to why you are leaning towards saying goodbye love, instead of stamping your reason on the door of my heart for why we shall always and forever remain together in your secret garden. Let us not get it twisted; I love you, but I am mad as hell with your lack of care and concern with how you display your love for me. My insecurities in you have superseded my expectations of you, leaving me with little to no motivation to be the lover you want, let alone the one I know you need. I used to want to be not your part time, but your full-time lover, ready in the words of Tonie, Tony, Toni to do whatever you wanted, because I thought you would provide a sense of stability that would encourage the woman you expected me to be to show up naturally. Instead, you act like Rick James and like I am, that word that rhymes with witch but starts with a "b."

I committed to being your wife, not your concubine; I will be your super freak but not your hoe. You wonder why my sexy freak chooses not to come out at night to pay you a conjugal visit? Maybe you need to do a better job handling her when you pull her out from the secret lair of my caged heart. Listen, I never meant to cause you any problems, and I never meant to cause you any pain, for that I truly, truly am sorry, but honestly, this journey with you has not been an easy walk in the park I would necessarily like to take back down memory lane again.

You need to remember that I am the grass you chose, and no matter how much greener the grass on the other side appears to be, learn how to cut your own. Somebody on that side might just be taking a little better care of their grass than you are taking care of yours. I am your garden! Commit, like a good gardener, to the upkeep, maintenance, care, and love for the grass you have chosen. Invest in me and sow seeds of affirmation into your garden showing how much you cherish me and causing others to admire the beauty of your landscape. If you have never heard me before, can you hear me? Can you hear me now?

I, therefore, declare that when I vowed to love you for better or worse, for richer or poorer, in sickness and in health, and until death do us part, I guaranteed my end of the bargain by applying for fireproof insurance. Everything we lost in the fire, I know we can recover from because all the lessons we learned while going through the fire have been secured under my insurance coverage. So then Mr. Superhero Lover, I will wait patiently, no matter how long it takes, for you to come back to me from that place in our relationship where I abandoned you, and you return unto me with the joy of the man I forgot to love, the man I refuse to live without. I do not care how you get here; just get here when you can. So then, I ask you this day do you choose to love me or do you love me not no more?

With an awe stunned amazement, surprised after having heard those words from her mouth that he has longed to hear, "I'm so-r-r-r-r-r-ray," the Superhero once again discovers that she has managed to place the burden of their relationship's continuity upon the fragile shoulders of his unstable double minded posture. "Do I still love her, or do I love her not no more?" The pinnacle of all the relationship defining questions has arrived unexpectedly at his door, belligerently knocking and causing him to run on, carelessly, to see if this is the end and if so what is it going to be.

The shifting in between fantasy and reality, due largely in part to those manly insecurities discovered while going through the fire, has caused him at times to lose focus of the "We" in the question What are we, more concerned with "What should I do" under minding the value of her presence in the details of his future. Unsure, pondering within his thoughts if this is still where he wants to be, the Superhero Lover moves cautiously to release a statement in response to the post-fire comments said about him over to the press of the only reporter fit to handle the details of this story, Mrs. Destiny! As he starts on his long approach towards the table of decision, to deliver his response to her request in person, he favoring the once undeniably sexually chocolate flavor he told everyone he could not live without, now tempted by the alluring deception of lust false promise of how much better life might be without her, seeks first to explain his decision to love her or love her not no more before justifying his conclusion.

"Smothered by the flames of a fire I did not set nor could I predict; I sought to maneuver my way through the unknowns of our relationship obstacles by seeking out whatever means necessary for us to escape unharmed from the heat of our afflicted furnace. Before the fire you, how should I say, had your mind right, body tight, and were ready to make love every night! You had the glow of a superstar shining in the spotlight, and had me excitedly chanting, when you use to walk by with a tee shirt and your thong panties on, in the words of comedian Kevin Hart, "Alright, Alright, Alright!"

With your heavenly eyes always fixed on me, looking out for me like you were my own personal secret service agent and I was your president, you became a safe escape for me to vent my areas of vulnerability. Yes, the way you moved, the way you talked, the way you used to say my name, thank yah Jessie Powell, had me declaring that our love, without question, was a sure thing. See I just knew you were supposed to be the only drink strong enough to quench my thirst. My delicious Apple Bottom Pie crafted in an image I needed to satisfy my once out of control appetite, and the only high octane fuel, I use as my adrenalin rush to rev up my spiritual, intellectual, and sexual engines.

The first time I thought I saw your face I asked myself, without any hesitation, just why couldn't we be happily ever after? It is unfortunate that ecstasies reality, found at the beginning of every new relationship horizon, is met by the inevitable reality of every sunny day setting into the darkness of the night's unknown. I am lost for words, unable to explain how love shines so brightly in the day, but the ink with which it has beautifully tattooed the Earth's canvas fades away into the deception of human nature's reaction to love without light. The ease with which we love in those sunny days has caused us to neglect the strength of love's character and the glory of its smile lighting up the beauty of our night sky.

With the reflection of its expected results obscured, love sometimes loses its composure illegally conceding to the will of the dark side, a place where its glory is misunderstood and regularly under appreciated. The ignorance of us unlearned in the languages of love, has caused the light of our love to be eclipsed by this darker side that continues to encourage us to thoughtlessly pledge the allegiance of our love to one another without the knowledge of its application. The question then is not if whether I love you or love you not no more, but rather have I loved you according to the language of your love and if not am I possessed with the unusual ability to, after reexamining if whether the debt to income margin for continuing in this love relationship is worth my investment. Is loving you worth the time, energy, and effort of a demand you presupposed I would, without any confrontation, resign the authority of my manhood over to?

You have, whether on purpose or by accident, tried to convince me to conform to the distorted perception of an image I was created by God to represent, manhood. Your list of conditions upon which you require me to abide by has caused you to undermine my authority as head of the house, emancipating yourself into the image of an unsubmitted wife basking in an unauthorized fanatical liberty that thrives on a notion that promises you a false sense of entitlement. You seek now to provide me, your husband, with those due benevolent benefits you should be so happy to grant, only when I, in my response to your request, without resistance, conform to your idea of a whimpering man with no backbone. You expect me to think like you, and see things from your point of view, refusing me the liberty of my husbandly rights, boycotting and protesting for you, my wife, to be considered worthy enough for me to submit up under you as the head of our home. Under valuing the measures of my continued contribution towards your well better behalf, you have dismissed the efforts of the rewards bestowed upon you with a sarcastic smile and a resentful posture towards me that openly declares that until I do right by you, you would choose rather to criticize the gifts I have given, when not aligned with the standard of your expectation.

When I think you are listening, your demeanor shows you are disinterested, consumed with the pleasure of all others, even at the expense of me, the other supposed to be more significant than all the rest. I know that while in the fire, I let go of your hand and lost focus of you for an extended length of time that left you with a wound that will always remind and cause you to resent me for my absence. I never left you in the fire by yourself, but I did let go of your hand and for that, I am so, so sorry. As you hold off and hold out until you get a justifiable answer to your question of why did I let go of you hand, to which you believe you are over zealously entitled, I pray you would one day understand that it was the most reasonable way I thought at that time for the both of us to escape with the least likely possibility of fatality.

With that said, I must say that I feel that the tragedy of the fire and the overwhelming exposure of one another's dysfunctional personality may have been just too much for us to get over and back to where things used to be. Can our love ever live in the memory of what it once was before and should we both seek to esteem love as the threaded cord that unites two dysfunctional powers to become one flesh? Have we, at this point in our relationship seen too much for us to pursue after love and recover all?

"I therefore announce that in the case of "The Superhero Lover: He Loves Me or He Loves Me Not No More," File Number 1119673, I, the Superhero Lover, declare to the Sexy and Vivacious Mrs. Destiny Lover that when it comes to loving you or loving you not no more, I announce that I, that I choose to, to, to……………………………………………………"

To be continued…………………….

Other Books by the Author

Available in retail stores, on www.amazon.com and
www.barnes&noble.com, and wherever books are sold.
(ISBN 978-0-615-65497-3)

Available in retail stores, on www.amazon.com and
www.barnes&noble.com, and wherever books are sold.

(ISBN 978-0-692-02244-3)

Contact Information

To inquire about Pastor Shaun Saunders speaking, ministering, or doing book signings and discussions at your event, you may contact him by sending an email to:

thesuperherolover@gmail.com

Connect with him on Twitter:

@ssaundersauthor

Printed in the USA
CPSIA information can be obtained
at www.ICGtesting.com
JSHW010722240324
59620JS00011B/128